LOO LAUGHS

WHILE YOU POOP

Thank you for shopping with us!

Please remember to leave your honest *REVIEW* because your opinion can help others and me, build a better community.

Scan this QR Code if you want to be part of our community and be the first to know when new books appear.

BONUS
Number Search Games

Welcome to the Wacky World of Puzzles and Laughs!

In this quirky book, prepare yourself for a rollercoaster of hilarity and brain-teasing challenges.

We've mixed the best of riddles, jokes, mazes, word scrambles, word searches, puzzles, and funny facts to keep you entertained for hours. 💩 Ok, at list one.

Get ready to laugh, scratch your head, and have a blast as you navigate through this delightful puzzle paradise.

Side note:
Leave your phone outside and take a pencil with you.

PLEASE REMAIN SEATED FOR THE ENTIRE PERFORMANCE
THANK YOU!

MULTIPLY AND ADD THE NUMBERS FROM 1 TO 9, INCLUSIVE, TO GIVE 100, BUT EACH NUMBER MUST BE USED ONLY ONCE.

READY, SET, GO!

WHAT GETS WETTER AS IT DRIES?

I CAN BE CRACKED, MADE, TOLD, AND PLAYED. WHAT AM I?

WHAT COMES ONCE IN A MINUTE, TWICE IN A MOMENT, BUT NEVER IN A THOUSAND YEARS?

WHAT CAN TAKE A TRIP AROUND THE GLOBE WITHOUT EVER LEAVING ITS SPOT?

WHAT HAS A HEART THAT DOESN'T BEAT?

A TOWEL.

A JOKE.

THE LETTER "M".

A STAMP.

AN ARTICHOKE.

D
O
N'
T

T

LOOK!

FILL IN THE MISSING LETTERS AND EACH OF THE FOLLOWING SERIES, AND YOU WILL DISCOVER THAT THEY REPRESENT A POPULAR PROVERB.

1. A-T-T-H-N-T-M-S-V-S-N-N.

2. F-I-T-H-A-T-E-E-W-N-A-R-A-Y.

3. S-R-K-W-I-E-H-I-O-S-H-T.

4. H-1-G-S-B-S-W-O-A-G-S-1-T.

5. B-R-S-F-F-T-R-F-C-T-G-T-R.

6. H-W-O-G-S-B-R'-W-G-G-S-S-R-W-G.

FIND THE DIFFERENCE

-ONLY ONE TILE

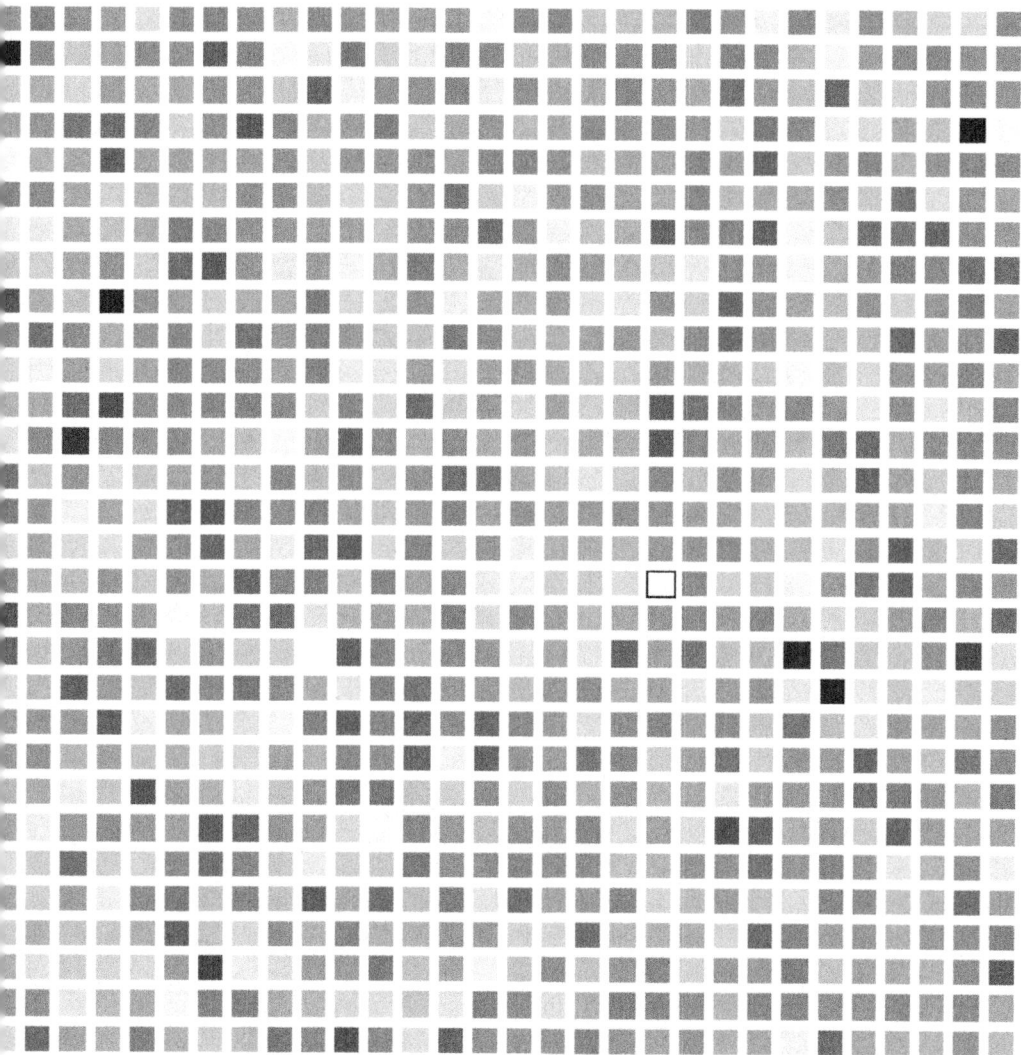

- [ ] SOAP
- [ ] TOOTHPASTE
- [ ] RAZOR
- [ ] FLOSS
- [ ] TOWEL
- [ ] SHAMPOO
- [ ] SINK
- [ ] TOILET
- [ ] MIRROR
- [ ] SPONGE

LOOK FOR WORDS IN ALL DIRECTIONS, LEFT TO RIGHT, AND VICE VERSA.

M	P	U	S	Q	B	T	U	O	Q	F	J	E	G	Q
R	P	Q	V	T	P	R	C	O	O	I	Q	O	K	C
K	M	I	R	R	O	R	A	P	Q	Y	O	H	M	N
X	S	U	W	Z	Q	O	X	M	J	I	H	H	P	G
W	G	P	A	S	S	I	T	A	K	P	J	F	N	S
A	X	R	A	X	N	V	X	H	A	G	M	H	B	L
W	S	V	Z	B	A	T	G	S	P	U	C	S	H	W
J	B	L	P	T	E	D	P	T	T	A	R	G	E	S
A	R	E	K	L	J	O	U	P	C	U	S	N	G	I
Y	X	W	I	N	N	J	A	O	A	V	S	T	Q	L
W	P	O	E	G	I	O	N	N	U	B	O	H	E	T
D	T	T	E	P	S	S	B	C	M	W	L	R	F	G
W	I	N	J	B	O	P	Q	N	K	C	F	B	B	D
J	L	M	U	F	N	X	M	K	G	R	H	E	H	A
M	M	H	Q	D	I	N	N	P	J	Z	Y	V	R	L

CAN YOU UNSCRAMBLE THESE WORDS?

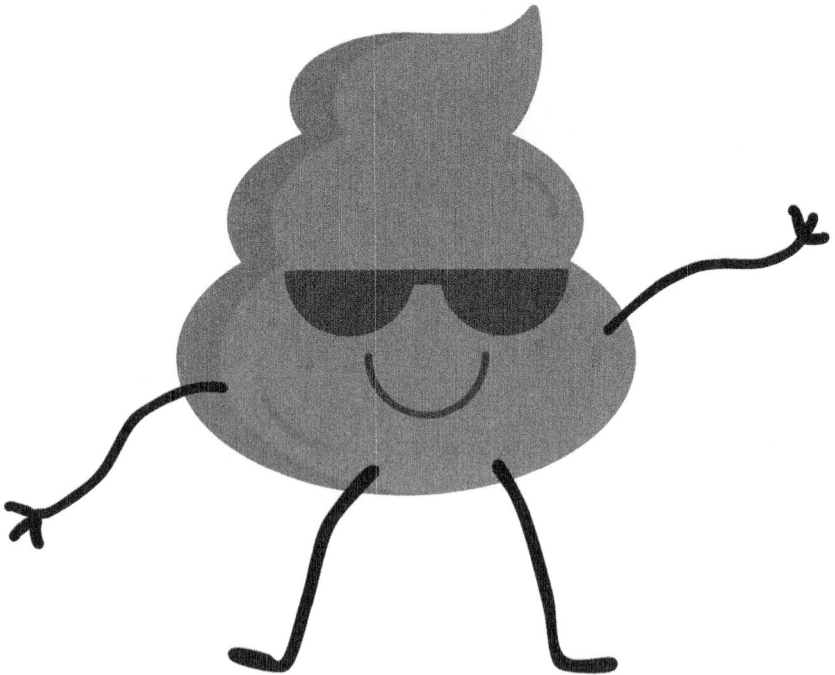

YES, YOU CAN!!

egiDlht	= _____	rCimhasa	= _____
amnulelitl	= _____	lieGagmn	= _____
anromouisH	= _____	tnejvaReue	= _____
ebiuleJ	= _____	elyvLi	= _____
upraeEnrt	= _____	tqeixsuiE	= _____
anRdciae	= _____	yRasdohp	= _____
wdWilnhir	= _____	eihvrT	= _____
stZe	= _____	soicuVvia	= _____
ubnicaeJl	= _____	cEtssay	= _____
mSeiblu	= _____	ciproEuh	= _____
rhpyeZ	= _____	sinEovin	= _____
rtinglGeti	= _____	giraMe	= _____
eNcart	= _____	Ossai	= _____
nItfneii	= _____	otUpai	= _____
tacliDee	= _____	Gmela	= _____
vigenraolt	= _____	zQlziauci	= _____
goytrraCpm	= _____	loWirstd	= _____
Mysytre	= _____	epPrelx	= _____
onpyrEt	= _____	Srtam	= _____
Cervle	= _____	ealnMt	= _____

13

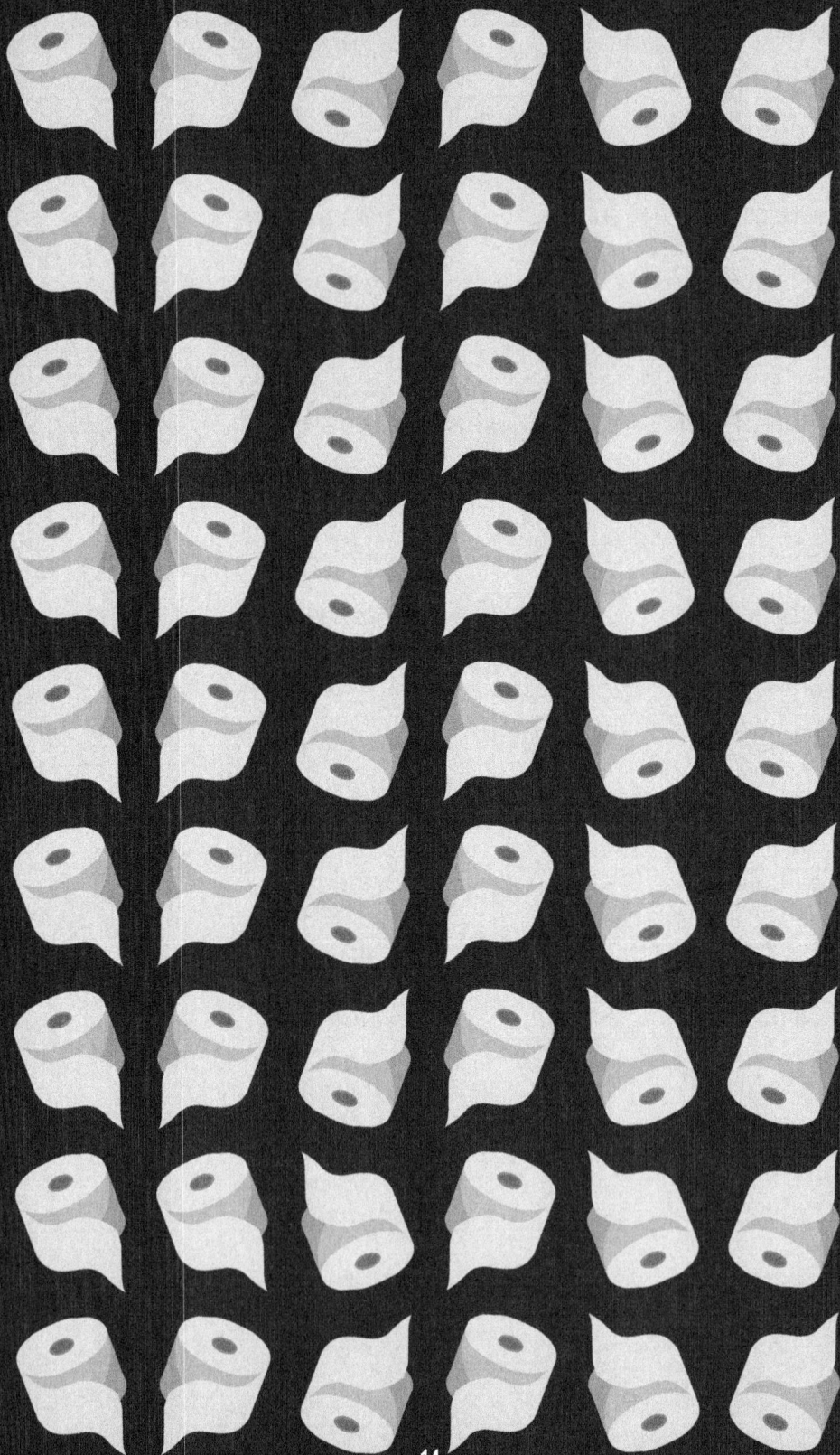

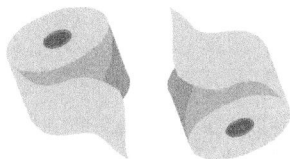

THIS PAIR ONLY APPEARS
ONCE.

CAN YOU FIND IT?

YOU CAN CUT THEM

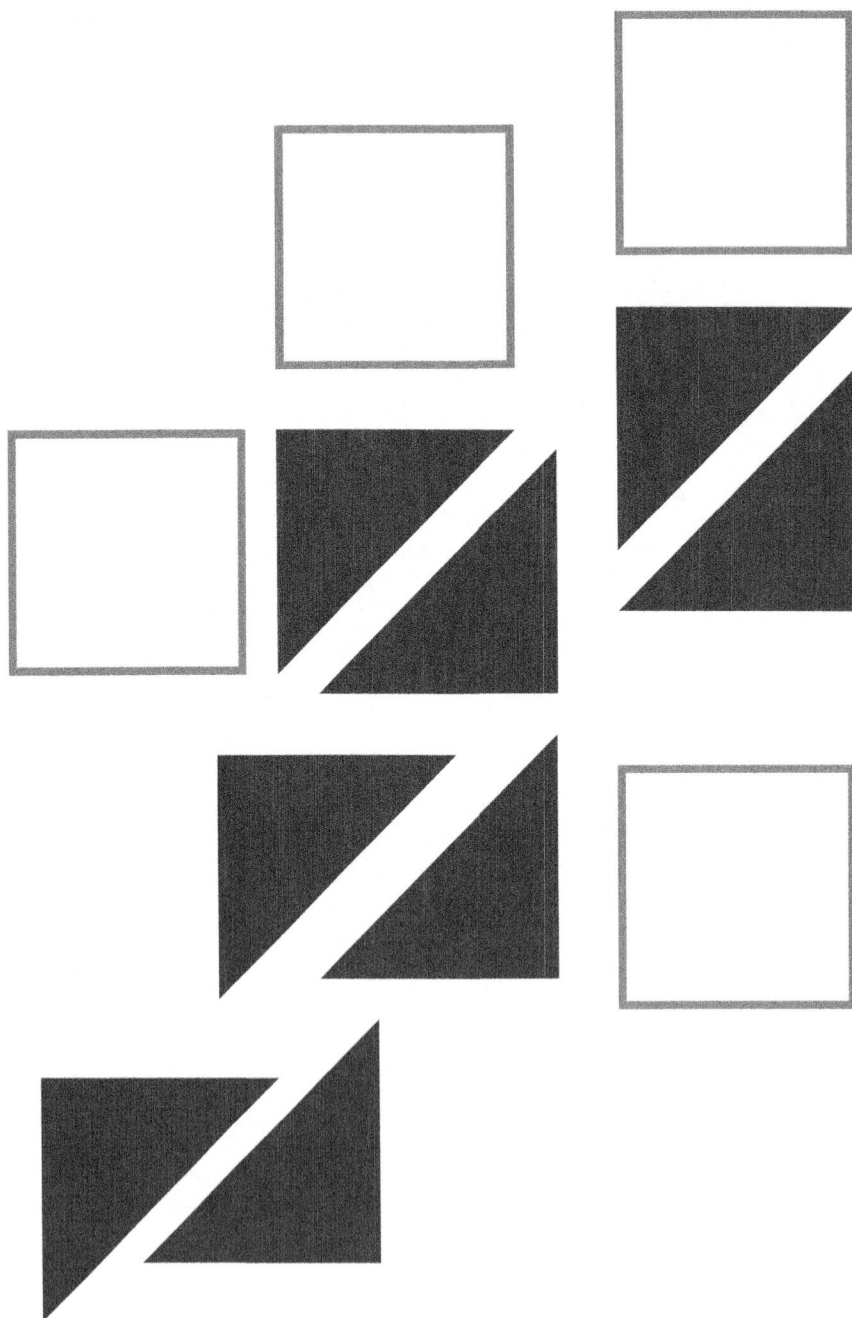

YOU HAVE 12 GEOMETRIC SHAPES: SQUARES AND TRIANGLES. TRIANGLES ARE FORMED BY CUTTING SQUARES DIAGONALLY.

CAN YOU ARRANGE THEM SO THAT YOU HAVE A PERFECT SQUARE?

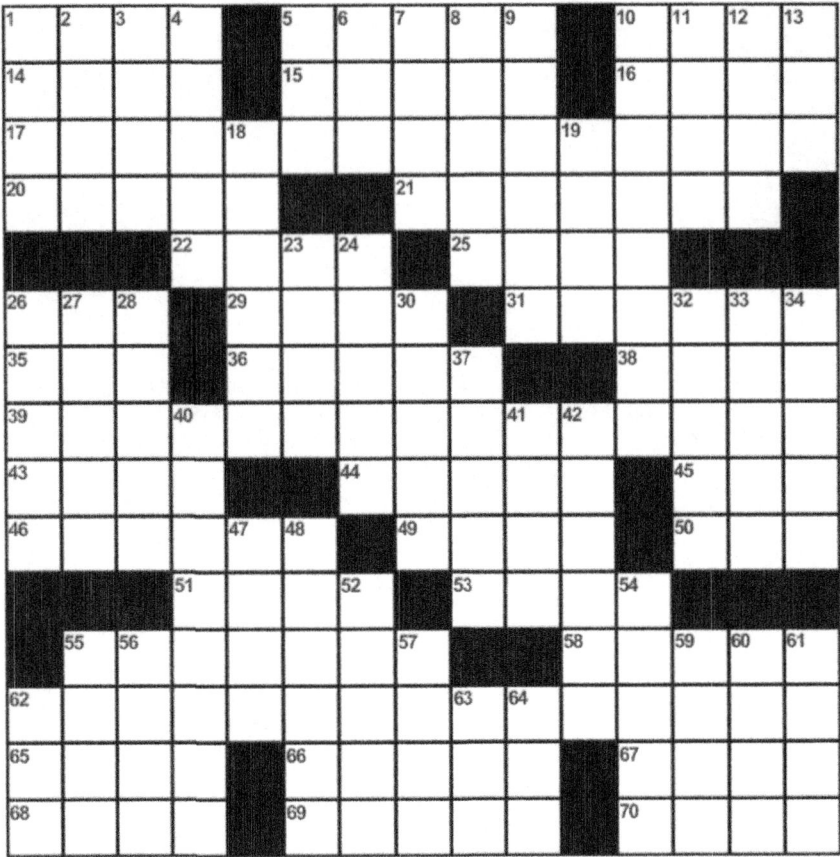

ACROSS

1) End-of-song feature
5) Earthenware containers
10) Hushed "Hey, you!"
14) ___ out a living (barely scraped by)
15) Fling mightily
16) Arab bigwig
17) Business efficiency technique

20) Jung's feminine personality
21) Argument
22) Siam visitor
25) Negotiator's goal
26) "Things that Make You Go ___"
29) Bauble
31) Buy as soon as available
35) "Yes, captain"
36) Works as a stevedore
38) Far from a few
39) Without a second to spare

CROSSWORD

DOWN

1) Cheese you can crumble
2) Of the same family
3) Prefix meaning "half"
4) Abnormal swelling
5) "How about that!"
6) Net-tipping serve
7) "The best-___ schemes ..."
8) Keep from happening
9) Feels intuitively
10) Irritated by the littlest things
11) Obscene material
12) Half of an argument
13) Hear, as a case
18) Old laundry appliance
19) Pinkie-to-thumb measure
23) Flatbread of India
24) It's mastered in a studio
26) Hispaniola half
27) Mocking birds
28) Urban area, briefly
30) They have four suits
32) Calmness
33) Deprive of courage
34) Henhouse sounds
37) Hit the ice
40) 63-gallon cask
41) Australia's national gemstone
42) Less flabby
47) Stew or miscellany
48) Like some yogurt
52) Hunk of cheese
54) Tempter of men's souls
55) Electricity carrier
56) Sherman Hemsley sitcom
57) Clothes line
59) Revered leader
60) Ms. Brockovich
61) Certain National League team
62) Indexing aid
63) Any singer behind Gladys Knight
64) Picnic pest

ACROSS

43) Polynesian food
44) Giraffelike beast
45) Drain, as of resources
46) Equilateral triangle, e.g.
49) "You are here" symbol
50) Jr. naval officer
51) Decelerate
53) Very common trees
55) Young hula dancers
58) Ready to rock
62) It may be up in the air at an airport
65) General surroundings
66) "To repeat ..."
67) Like a desert
68) Assume a stooped posture
69) Offer chocolates to, as a dieter
70) Mother's helpers?

THE OBJECTIVE OF THE GAME IS TO FILL THE GRID WITH NUMBERS FROM 1 TO 5, SUCH THAT EACH ROW AND COLUMN CONTAINS EACH NUMBER EXACTLY ONCE.

ADDITIONALLY, THE GRID CONTAINS INEQUALITY SIGNS (< AND >) BETWEEN SOME CELLS. THESE SIGNS INDICATE THAT THE NUMBER IN THE CELL ON THE LEFT OR ABOVE IS SMALLER OR LARGER THAN THE NUMBER IN THE CELL ON THE RIGHT OR BELOW, AND VICE VERSA.

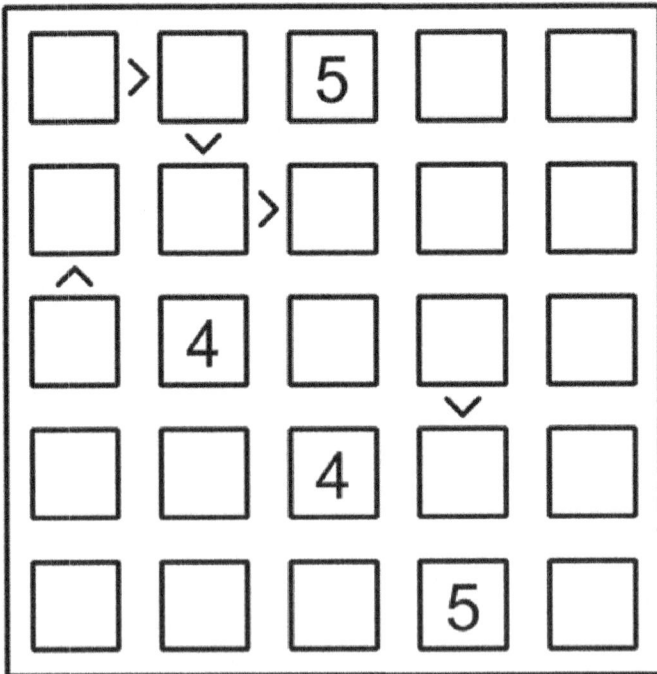

☐ > ☐		5	☐	☐
☐ ∨ ☐ > ☐			☐	☐
☐ ∧	4	☐	☐	☐
☐	☐	4	☐ ∨	☐
☐	☐	☐	5	☐

FUTOSHIKI

20

WHAT'S A VAMPIRE'S FAVORITE ROOM IN THE HOUSE?

THE BAT-ROOM!

WHY DID THE TOILET PAPER ROLL DOWN THE HILL?

BECAUSE IT WANTED TO GET TO THE BOTTOM!

WHAT DO YOU CALL A BATHROOM SUPERHERO?

FLUSH GORDON!

WHAT HAPPENS in the bathroom STAYS IN THE BATHROOM

THE MORE YOU TAKE, THE MORE YOU LEAVE BEHIND. WHAT AM I?

I SPEAK WITHOUT A MOUTH AND HEAR WITHOUT EARS. I HAVE NO BODY, BUT I COME ALIVE WITH THE WIND. WHAT AM I?

WHAT IS FULL OF HOLES BUT STILL HOLDS A LOT OF WEIGHT?

WHAT HAS KEYS BUT CAN'T OPEN LOCKS?

WHAT HAS ONE EYE BUT CAN'T SEE?

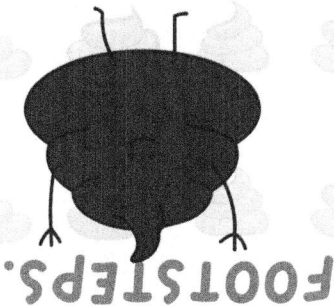

FOOTSTEPS.

AN ECHO.

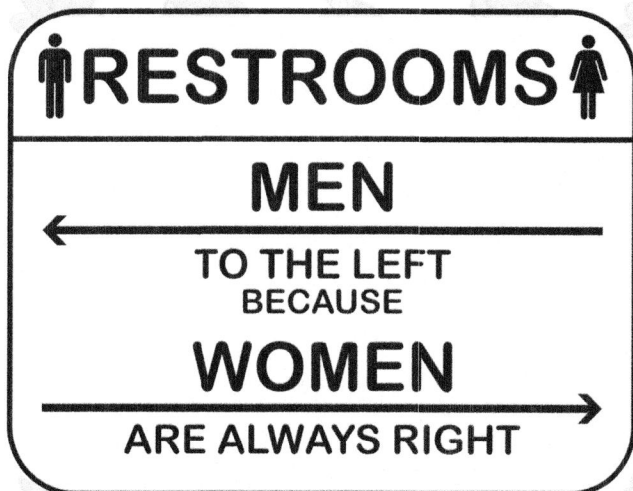

RESTROOMS

MEN
← TO THE LEFT
BECAUSE
WOMEN
ARE ALWAYS RIGHT →

A NET.

A PIANO.

A NEEDLE.

POO RIDDLE

25

FIND THIS SEQUENCE OF
TOILETS

- [ ] NUMBER ONE
- [ ] LOO
- [ ] WASHROOM
- [ ] COMMODE
- [ ] THRONE
- [ ] RESTROOM
- [ ] LAVATORY
- [ ] PORCELAIN
- [ ] POTTY
- [ ] JOHN

WORD SEARCH

LOOK FOR WORDS IN ALL DIRECTIONS, LEFT TO RIGHT, AND VICE VERSA.

B	Z	F	C	J	Z	O	Y	O	N	T	C	N	C
R	N	K	H	X	V	E	L	N	K	E	C	H	Z
N	O	U	Y	T	J	P	D	Z	C	J	X	U	D
G	H	I	M	L	I	T	R	O	M	D	J	J	K
X	K	O	P	B	C	M	W	O	M	R	R	P	Y
C	R	F	J	Y	E	N	O	C	J	M	G	O	E
L	A	V	A	T	O	R	Y	O	F	J	O	R	G
Y	B	H	L	W	T	H	O	E	R	O	I	C	N
X	T	H	X	S	X	G	R	N	P	H	O	E	W
B	Q	F	E	J	X	N	L	O	E	E	S	L	P
I	R	R	Q	N	R	N	T	R	X	X	C	A	S
X	X	W	W	W	V	T	J	H	H	S	T	I	W
H	G	B	J	M	Y	G	I	T	A	G	G	N	F
I	H	W	R	E	G	Q	Q	D	U	T	R	Y	P

CAN YOU UNSCRAMBLE THESE WORDS?

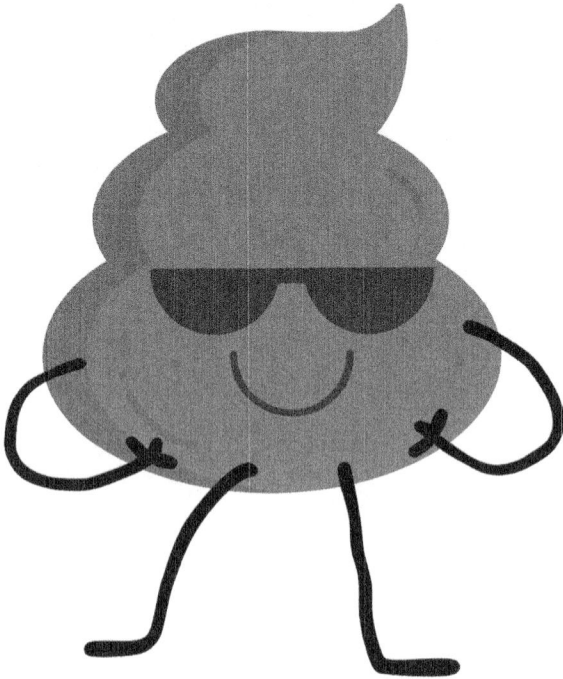

dAreutvne	= _____	hSnseiun	= _____
arerancgF	= _____	nEpletah	= _____
nhSpoymy	= _____	uftlreytB	= _____
caetoohCl	= _____	itoeatnMdi	= _____
aHenspisp	= _____	srUvniee	= _____
tnliuTyriaq	= _____	npedytrieSi	= _____
hmtEnssaui	= _____	Piobtiyssil	= _____
Crtuiiyso	= _____	cfetnioelR	= _____
nVratib	= _____	uaioniblJt	= _____
yaHonmr	= _____	edorWn	= _____
gtLeruha	= _____	rpihFisden	= _____
mssoBlo	= _____	uhiEoarp	= _____
ovalerMsu	= _____	tintgCipaav	= _____
klraeSp	= _____	iadtRan	= _____
yodMle	= _____	eCscaad	= _____
closuaiMru	= _____	Dtguefhlil	= _____
dmorFee	= _____	ieyeSrnt	= _____
mosiunLu	= _____	ieeenslRic	= _____
Tiaqlnur	= _____	danlndoWre	= _____
Bintilrla	= _____	anrispniolt	= _____

USING TWO STRAIGHT LINES,
YOU WILL FORM OTHER
SHAPES THAT, WHEN JOINED,
WILL GIVE A SQUARE.

CAN YOU FIGURE OUT THE
ANSWER IN A MINUTE?

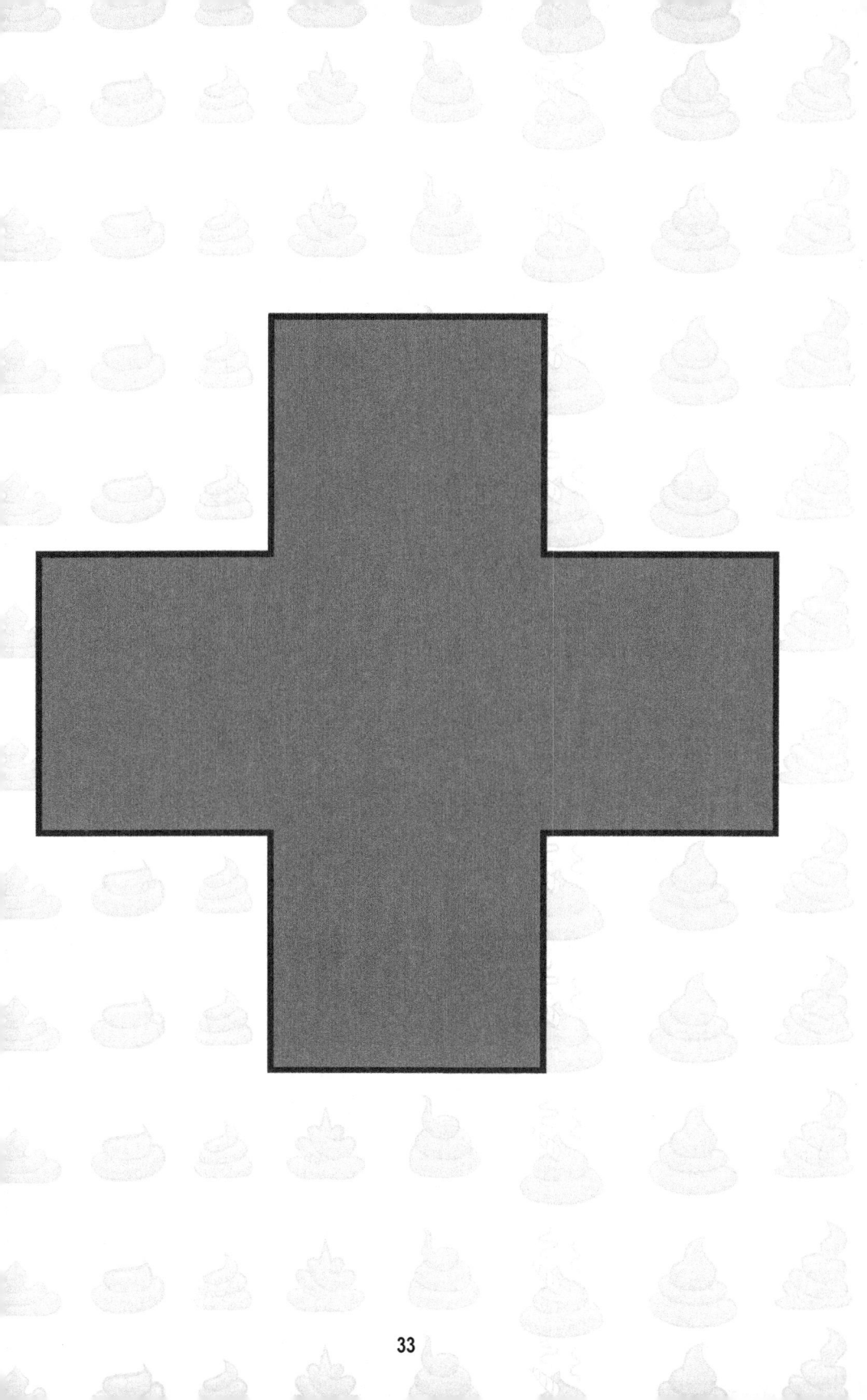

ARRANGE THE NUMBERS FROM 1 TO 9, INCLUSIVE, IN THE FORM OF A SQUARE SO THAT THE TOTAL OF EACH LINE, HORIZONTAL, VERTICAL, OR DIAGONAL, IS THE SAME.

IT'S INTERESTING THAT YOU CAN DO THAT, RIGHT?

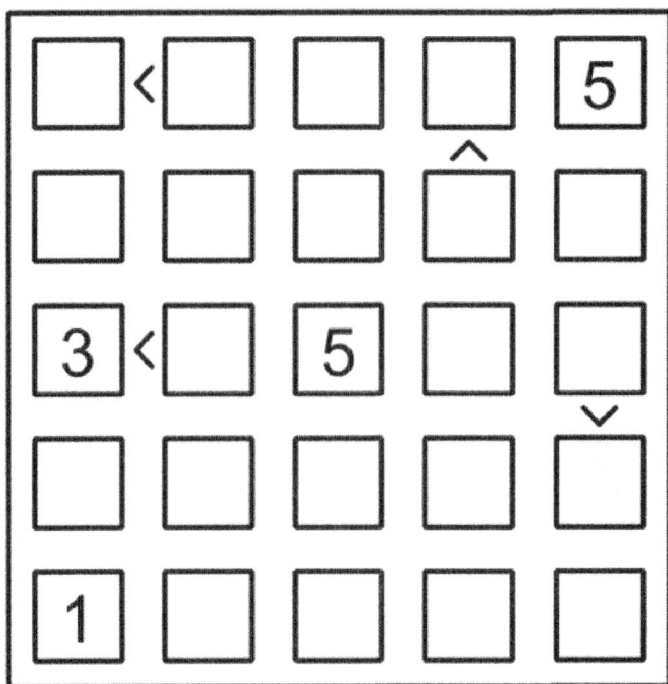

FIND THE DIFFERENCES

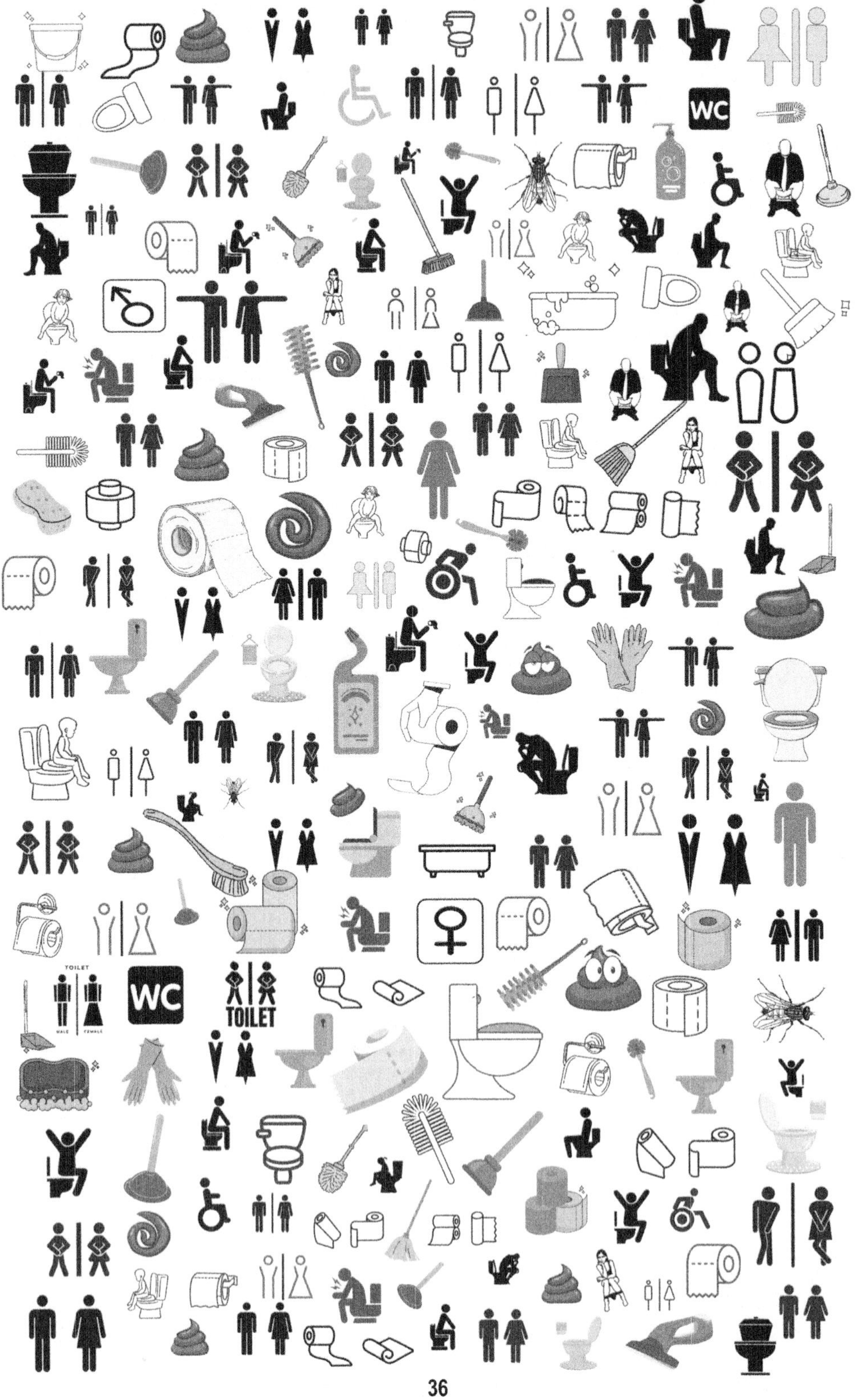

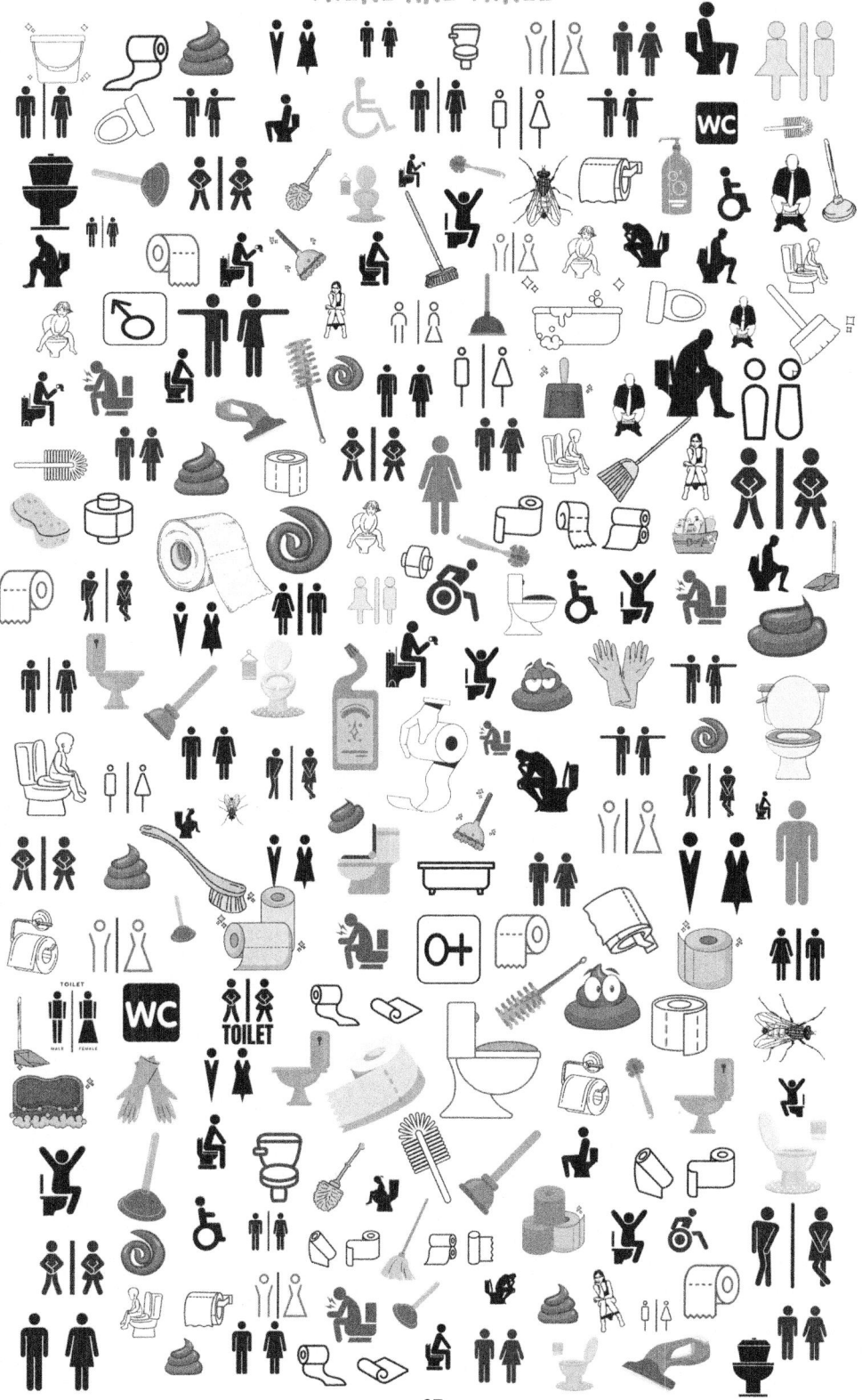

WHAT CAN YOU CATCH BUT NOT THROW?

WHAT BELONGS TO YOU BUT OTHER PEOPLE USE IT MORE THAN YOU DO?

WHAT IS AS LIGHT AS A FEATHER, YET THE STRONGEST PERSON CAN'T HOLD IT FOR MUCH LONGER THAN A MINUTE?

WHAT HAS CITIES, BUT NO HOUSES; FORESTS, BUT NO TREES; AND RIVERS, BUT NO WATER?

CHANGING THE TOILET PAPER ROLL will not CAUSE brain DAMAGE

A MAP.

YOUR BREATH.

YOUR NAME.

A COLD.

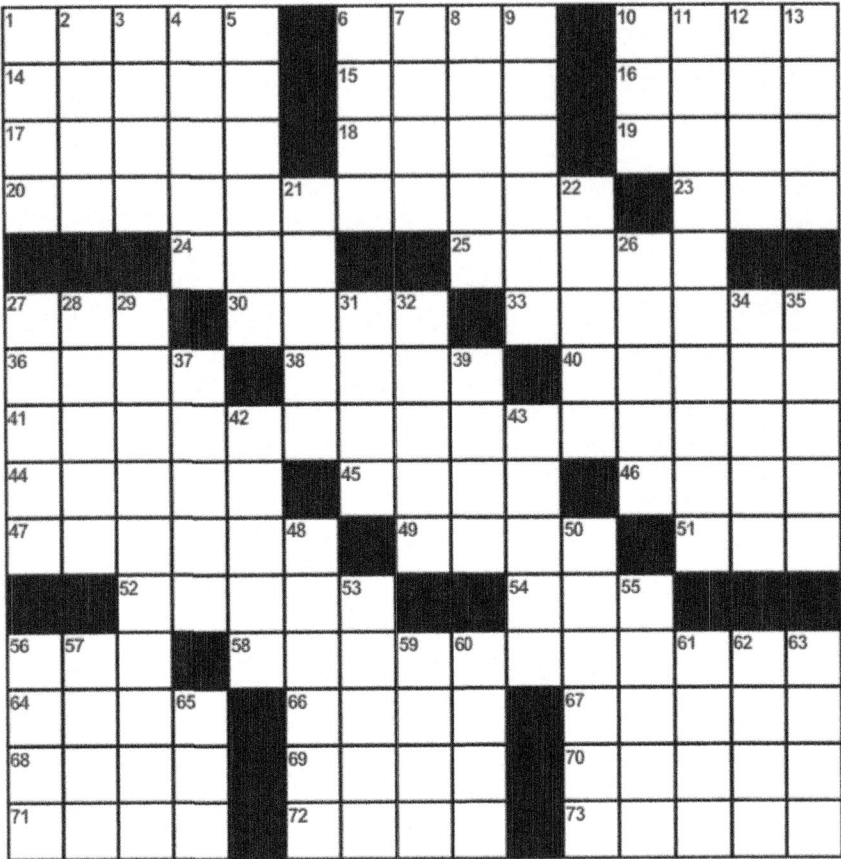

ACROSS

1) Spanish houses
6) No Westminster contender
10) Spheres
14) Irish actor Milo
15) Lot of rows to hoe?
16) Dry tobacco leaves, e.g.
17) Sovereign time period
18) ___ Bator, Mongolia
19) It's uplifting to a skier
20) Street magician of note
23) One that serves the queen
24) Acting Mineo
25) Showing effortless grace
27) "7 Faces of Dr. ___"
30) It can be more, proverbially
33) Part of a runner's garb
36) Edison's middle name
38) Prefix for the opposed
40) In spite of the fact, to poets
41) Guys with white tigers,
    once

DOWN

1) Firewood measure
2) Not on land
3) Homemade knife
4) Zeus' shield
5) Summer shoe
6) Badly claw
7) Bruins go there
8) Well-traveled path
9) Game that starts with love?
10) Start of the last qtr.?
11) Plant moved by an ant, in song
12) Hillside near Glasgow
13) Like the surface of Mercury
21) Make indistinct
22) Hawke of Hollywood
26) No ___ barred
27) Will Rogers' prop
28) Flying-saucer pilot
29) Outshine

31) Tizzy
32) Word before "fast" and after "home"
34) Rose protector
35) High-protein beans
37) Come to terms
39) Monty Python performer
42) Deadly
43) "... lion and goes out like ___"
48) Ski in a zigzag course
50) Like a system of serfs and lords
53) Type of drum
55) Foolish talk
56) Strait-laced
57) It's in the can, maybe
59) Good buddy?
60) In ___ (actually)
61) "Gone With the Wind" estate
62) Small bills
63) Subject of "A Beautiful Mind"
65) Camera type, for short

ACROSS

44) Famed missionary Junipero
45) Like any NBA center
46) Medical fluids
47) Commencements
49) Fall on ___ ears
51) One of Tennessee's twosomes
52) Gets better, as a wound
54) Yankee's crosstown rival
56) Socially conscious ad (abbr.)

58) Long-time Vegas showman
64) Eleven yards make two
66) Where white suits are the norm
67) Supreme Ross
68) "Matinee" or "Billy" follower
69) They're mined and refined
70) After, on the slopes
71) Bryn ___
72) A ___ formality
73) Pet-store purchase

43

I'M TALL WHEN I'M YOUNG, AND I'M SHORT WHEN I'M OLD. WHAT AM I?

WHAT HAS A NECK BUT NO HEAD?

WHAT HAS A THUMB AND FOUR FINGERS BUT IS NOT ALIVE?

WHAT HAS A HEAD, A TAIL, BUT NO BODY?

WHAT IS FULL OF HOLES BUT STILL HOLDS A LOT OF WATER?

A CANDLE.

A BOTTLE.

A GLOVE.

A COIN.

A SPONGE.

EMPLOYEE RESTROOM

My boss makes a dollar...
I make a dime...
So, I sit on the porcelain throne
and poop on company time.

POO RIDDLE

45

THIS PAIR ONLY APPEARS ONCE.

CAN YOU FIND IT?

WHY DID THE TOILET PAPER GO TO THE PARTY?

BECAUSE IT WANTED TO GET A LITTLE UNRAVELED!

WHAT DID ONE WALL SAY TO THE OTHER WALL IN THE BATHROOM?

"I'LL MEET YOU AT THE CORNER!"

WHAT DO YOU CALL A BEAR IN THE BATHROOM?

A GRIZZLY-POTTY.

DID YOU KNOW THAT:

BATHROOMS ARE ONE OF THE MOST DANGEROUS ROOMS IN A HOUSE, WITH OVER 200,000 ACCIDENTS OCCURRING EACH YEAR.

BATHROOMS ARE A GREAT PLACE TO SING BECAUSE OF THE ACOUSTICS CREATED BY THE TILES AND HARD SURFACES.

- [ ] SHOWER
- [ ] FLOSS
- [ ] READ
- [ ] PAMPER
- [ ] BRUSH
- [ ] SCRUB
- [ ] SING
- [ ] FLUSH
- [ ] SHAVE
- [ ] RELAX

WORD SEARCH

LOOK FOR WORDS IN ALL DIRECTIONS, LEFT TO RIGHT, AND VICE VERSA.

P	Q	P	G	U	E	R	J	A	Y	B
A	J	D	D	C	L	I	E	J	E	D
M	M	S	M	K	F	R	O	A	S	Q
P	R	S	S	O	L	F	Q	P	D	X
E	J	A	M	A	U	H	L	M	P	A
R	E	W	O	H	S	V	O	M	T	L
F	V	A	E	U	H	C	N	D	R	E
U	A	T	R	B	A	G	R	C	E	R
Q	H	B	F	C	H	D	C	U	M	P
D	S	I	N	G	B	J	T	M	B	I
P	S	Y	Y	E	L	D	U	Q	Y	Y

CAN YOU UNSCRAMBLE THESE WORDS?

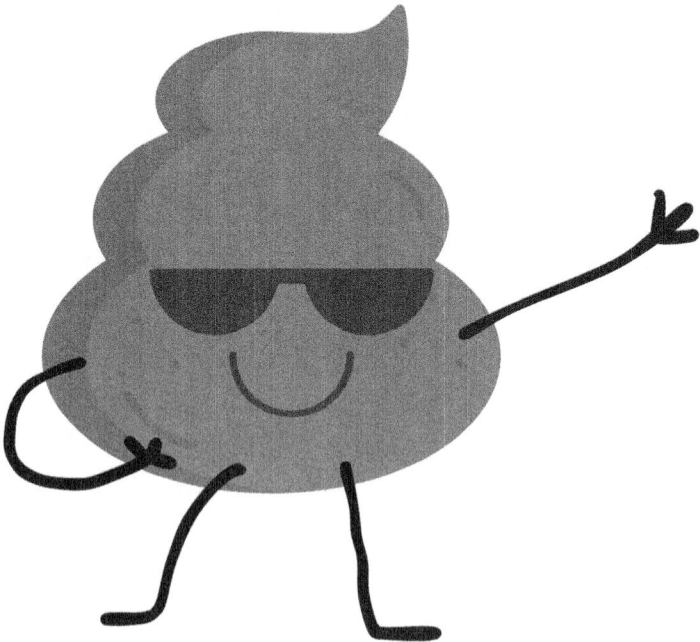

Wchislmai = _____   Buslsilf = _____

eeEetncvsffr = _____   gnMcteiinfa = _____

bnoRwia = _____   meScarlb = _____

zzuelP = _____   bmelJu = _____

Aarmgna = _____   eesrtLt = _____

snleabrUcm = _____   rBian = _____

olWpyrad = _____   aegaLnug = _____

eClu = _____   eagCllehn = _____

Regeaanrr = _____   lroaayucbV = _____

Wrmtodsih = _____   uonsfeC = _____

fSuhfle = _____   uesGs = _____

iMpxu = _____   gviSoln = _____

Txet = _____   tBnomarsri = _____

esaeT = _____   utiLsgsiinc = _____

idedRl = _____   oraedWgm = _____

gEmina = _____   pcrheeDi = _____

twsTi = _____   iptxteerCh = _____

rteSce = _____   nidHde = _____

eCdo = _____   odmaRn = _____

iLecnox = _____   tiycioDnra = _____

53

THE NUMBER 45 IS DIVIDED INTO FOUR PARTS, SO IF YOU ADD TWO TO THE FIRST, SUBTRACT TWO FROM THE SECOND, MULTIPLY THE THIRD BY TWO, AND DIVIDE THE FOURTH BY TWO, YOU WILL HAVE THE SAME RESULT EVERY TIME.

WHICH ARE THESE?

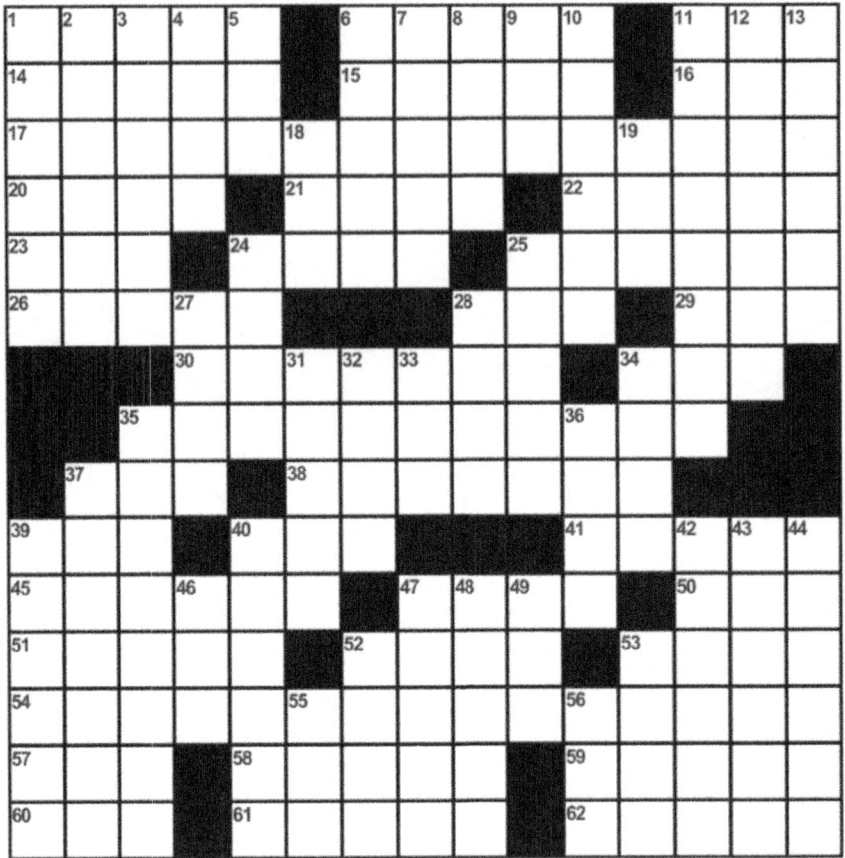

ACROSS

1) Not dormant
6) Brilliantly colored parrot
11) Word before or after "pack"
14) Argentine plain
15) Palate dangler
16) Jungle dweller
17) 1676 Virginia uprising
20) Knowledgeable about
21) Beef order
22) Insider talk
23) Frequent tattoo subject
24) Buildup at a river's mouth
25) Birdseed holder
26) Screw-up
28) Colt morsel
29) High-___ graphics
30) Change with the times, again
34) Distress signal
35) Asian restaurant serving

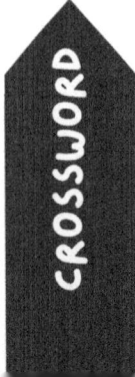

CROSSWORD

DOWN

1) LPs, e.g.
2) Apply hastily, as paint
3) Puget Sound city
4) Part of, as a practical joke
5) Director Howard
6) Wall decor
7) Head off, as disaster
8) Eight, to two
9) Draught drink
10) Billfold kin
11) Bit of drizzle
12) Certain orbital points
13) Pavarotti and Domingo
18) ___ Lanka
19) Be deceitful
24) Bird feeder food
25) Ayatollah's decree
27) Like some refills
28) Accessible to everyone
31) Cobwebby place
32) Harmonizing minimums

33) High card
34) Ad word
35) Wimbledon fault-caller
36) Breach of friendship
37) Native American baby
39) Patience, for one
40) Official who sings in Hebrew
42) ___ in (absorbing)
43) Gouda or brie
44) Holes that anchor ropes pass through
46) Spy org.
47) Barely discernible amount
48) Adds to the payroll
49) Singer DiFranco
52) Opposite of good
53) Dallas Cowboys emblem
55) The avant-garde's Yoko
56) Aussie bird

ACROSS

37) Popular dessert choice
38) Pedicure's target
39) Mover's truck
40) Successor org. to the USSR
41) Go get, to a dog
45) Drug for a poisoning victim
47) "All's Well ___ Ends Well"
50) "Caught you!"
51) Violin-bow application
52) "___ go bragh"
53) Distort, as survey results

54) Globe, cherry and roma
57) Dos Passos trilogy
58) Virtually guaranteed
59) Clergyman's quarters
60) Suffix for "Hallow"
61) Casting assignments
62) They can be hard to resist

LET ME REMIND YOU:

THE OBJECTIVE OF THE GAME IS TO FILL THE GRID WITH NUMBERS FROM 1 TO 5, SUCH THAT EACH ROW AND COLUMN CONTAINS EACH NUMBER EXACTLY ONCE.

ADDITIONALLY, THE GRID CONTAINS INEQUALITY SIGNS (< AND >) BETWEEN SOME CELLS. THESE SIGNS INDICATE THAT THE NUMBER IN THE CELL ON THE LEFT OR ABOVE IS SMALLER OR LARGER THAN THE NUMBER IN THE CELL ON THE RIGHT OR BELOW, AND VICE VERSA.

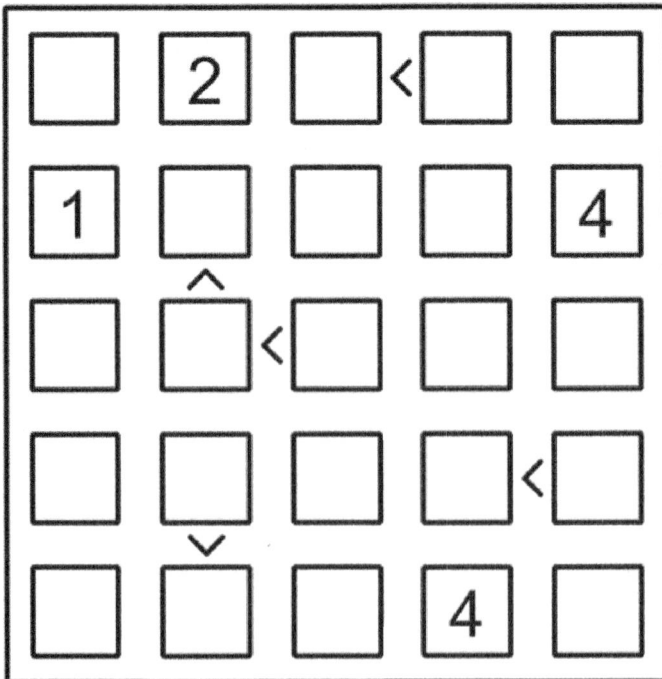

WHAT DO YOU CALL A BATHROOM ON A SPACESHIP?

AN ASTRO-LOO.

WHY DON'T SCIENTISTS TRUST ATOMS?

BECAUSE THEY MAKE UP EVERYTHING, EVEN THE BATHROOM!

WHY DID THE SHOWER GO TO THERAPY?

IT HAD TOO MANY ISSUES WITH ITS DRAIN.

EACH OF THE FOLLOWING LETTERS, WHEN PROPERLY ORDERED, WILL LEAD TO A POPULAR PROVERB.

A. AEEGGHILLMNNOOOORRSSSSTT.

B. AACEEEFFHHIIIIIMNOOOPRRSSTTTT.

C. AAADDEEFIIIMNNNNOORTTW.

D. AABBDDEEHHHHHIIIINNNOORRSSTTTTUUU.

FIND THE DIFFERENCE–ONLY ONE

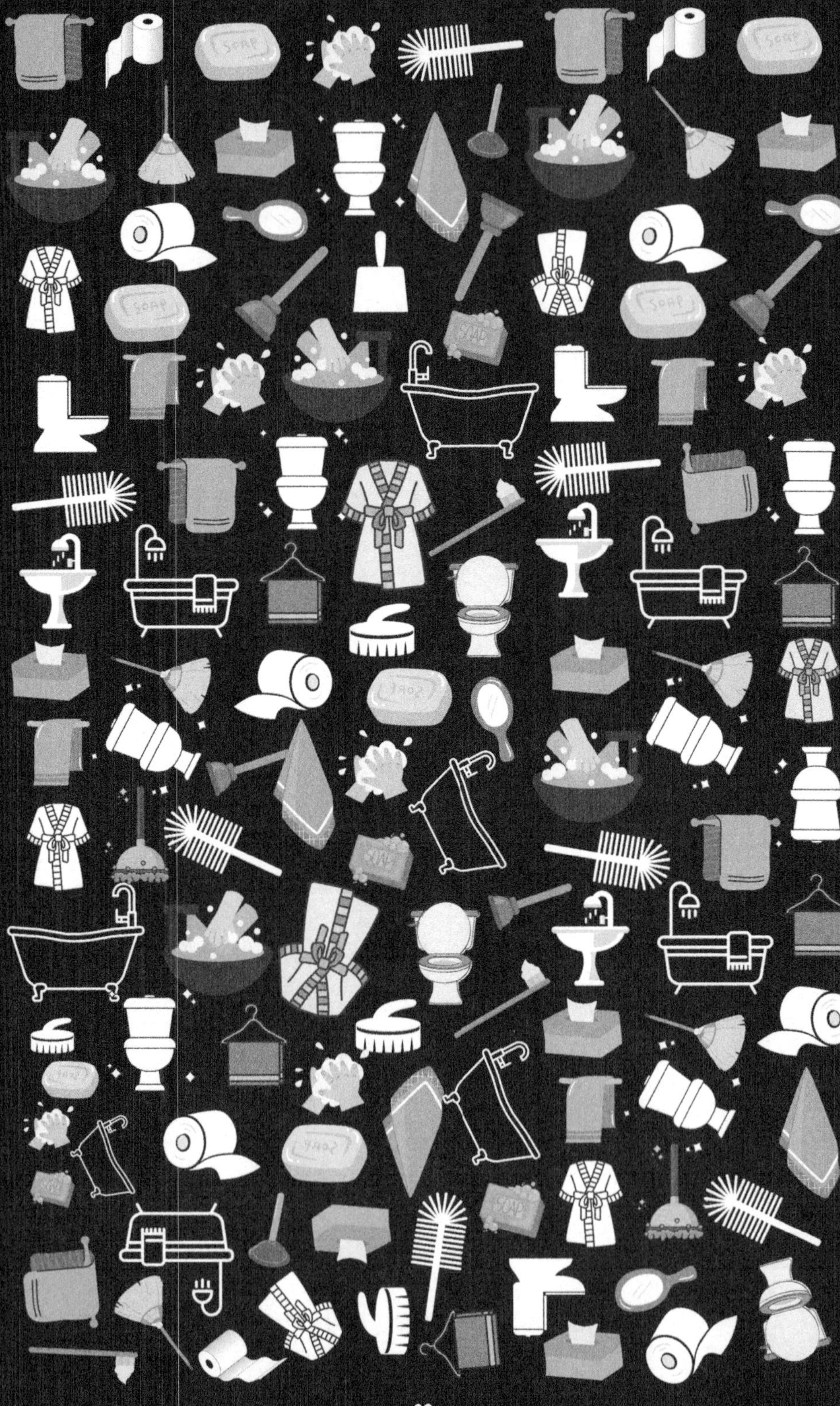

FINDS A NUMBER THAT IS MULTIPLIED BY 3, 6, 9, 12, 15, 18, 21, 24, OR 27 AND GIVES A RESULT CONSISTING OF 3 IDENTICAL DIGITS EACH TIME.

THIS PAIR ONLY APPEARS ONCE.

CAN YOU FIND IT?

FIND IN 40 SEC

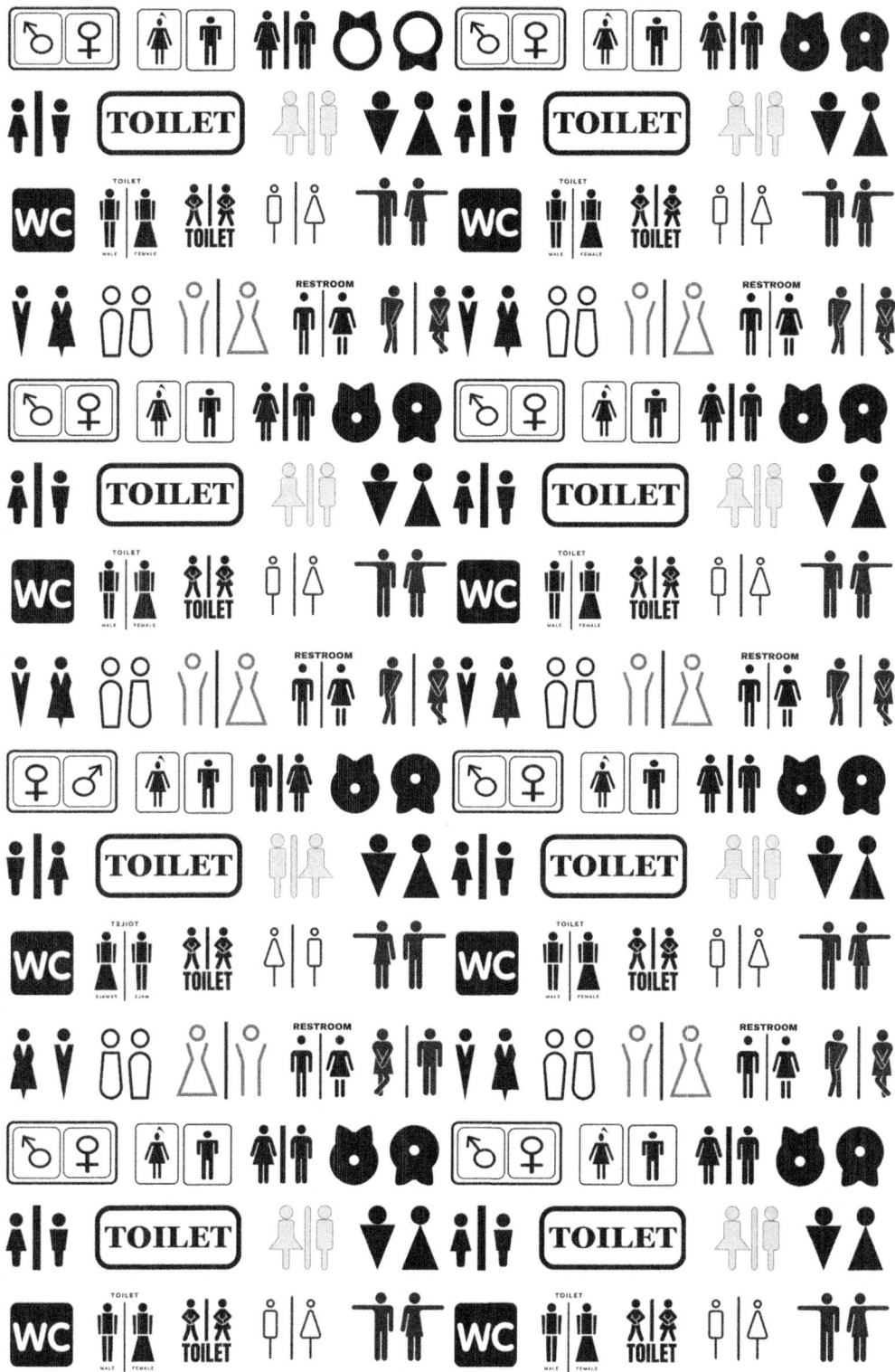

DID YOU KNOW THAT:

THE FIRST ELECTRIC TOOTHBRUSH WAS INVENTED IN 1939.

THE FIRST SHOWER CURTAIN WAS INVENTED IN 1937.

THE FIRST BATHTUB WITH BUILT-IN PLUMBING WAS INVENTED IN 1883.

THE FIRST MODERN TOILET WAS INVENTED BY THOMAS CRAPPER IN 1891.

- [ ] BIDET
- [ ] TOOTHBRUSH
- [ ] ELECTRIC RAZOR
- [ ] HAIRDRYER
- [ ] SHOWERHEAD
- [ ] BATH MAT
- [ ] AIR FRESHENER
- [ ] SCALE
- [ ] FAUCET
- [ ] PLUNGER

WORD SEARCH

LOOK FOR WORDS IN ALL DIRECTIONS, LEFT TO RIGHT, AND VICE VERSA.

I	P	R	T	W	M	O	R	D	T	X	E	S	Z	D	J	M	Y
G	E	E	V	V	L	A	D	I	X	T	T	D	Y	B	X	A	L
D	A	I	R	F	R	E	S	H	E	N	E	R	P	N	G	X	I
C	Q	L	C	X	K	Y	Q	E	C	B	J	D	O	G	Q	T	T
E	E	P	M	X	K	B	L	L	Q	K	G	A	I	Y	B	P	E
U	C	L	L	Q	J	O	G	A	P	O	V	H	Q	B	J	W	J
L	N	K	E	U	S	C	S	H	P	I	S	H	P	K	D	N
N	M	J	E	C	N	F	K	S	S	E	U	E	F	K	M	M	A
V	B	P	N	N	T	G	U	O	H	U	Z	T	I	V	N	Z	T
U	O	A	I	M	I	R	E	R	O	T	S	A	V	B	J	V	H
X	T	C	T	B	B	J	I	R	W	E	V	Y	N	U	S	N	N
Z	I	I	O	H	K	R	T	C	E	C	D	E	L	W	K	Q	O
P	W	P	T	H	M	V	F	J	R	U	W	T	Z	T	J	N	W
V	W	O	R	K	T	A	A	B	H	A	X	T	W	Z	Y	T	X
Y	O	T	E	O	X	D	T	S	E	F	Z	F	P	N	L	G	J
T	O	C	B	T	V	Z	Q	E	A	H	D	O	E	S	B	O	N
I	K	J	P	O	S	A	I	E	D	S	G	I	R	Z	F	M	I
S	V	N	U	J	Z	R	E	Y	R	D	R	I	A	H	Y	M	U

CAN YOU UNSCRAMBLE THESE WORDS?

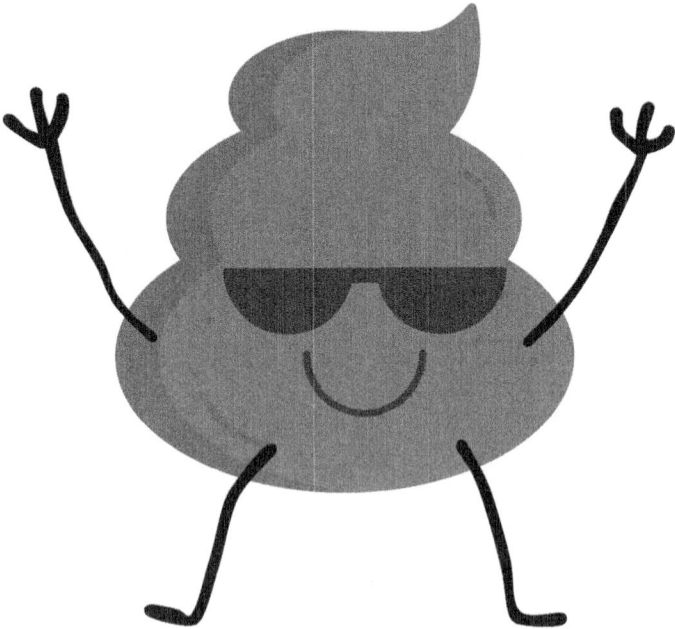

nleipgSl	= _____	kciTry	= _____
laPfluy	= _____	lteecnlgnlie	= _____
iulntpMaea	= _____	Cyxtliepom	= _____
Docsevyir	= _____	idbrndeenM	= _____
veriCeta	= _____	llCinheggan	= _____
uFn	= _____	nilgture	= _____
eMtisrsouy	= _____	binaelerotC	= _____
mgcatiEni	= _____	iCtrvaitye	= _____
ieSpnddl	= _____	oAinbmti	= _____
Dmcaiyn	= _____	olesignun	= _____
Groeusog	= _____	utZslfe	= _____
inolnonvta	= _____	Gsloouir	= _____
arouCogsue	= _____	cinnEnthga	= _____
aulntJib	= _____	nenahePlmo	= _____
nxuEbaetr	= _____	vaerlM	= _____
ntligrugni	= _____	ovaSr	= _____
feGacrul	= _____	ertlheEa	= _____
yrroPtpies	= _____	eArull	= _____
veeReir	= _____	rldeonpS	= _____
nPinaelc	= _____	Firolhsu	= _____

PRSVRYPRFCTMN
VRKPTHSPRCPTSTN.

THE UNUSUAL WRITING IS SAID TO BE FOUND IN THE CHANCEL OF A SMALL CHURCH IN WALES, JUST OVER THE TEN COMMANDMENTS. AMENDMENTS. THE INSERTION OF A SINGLE LETTER, REPEATED AT VARIOUS INTERVALS, NOT ONLY MAKES IT COMPREHENSIBLE BUT ALSO SUITED FOR THE SITUATION.

WHAT IS THE OMITTED LETTER?

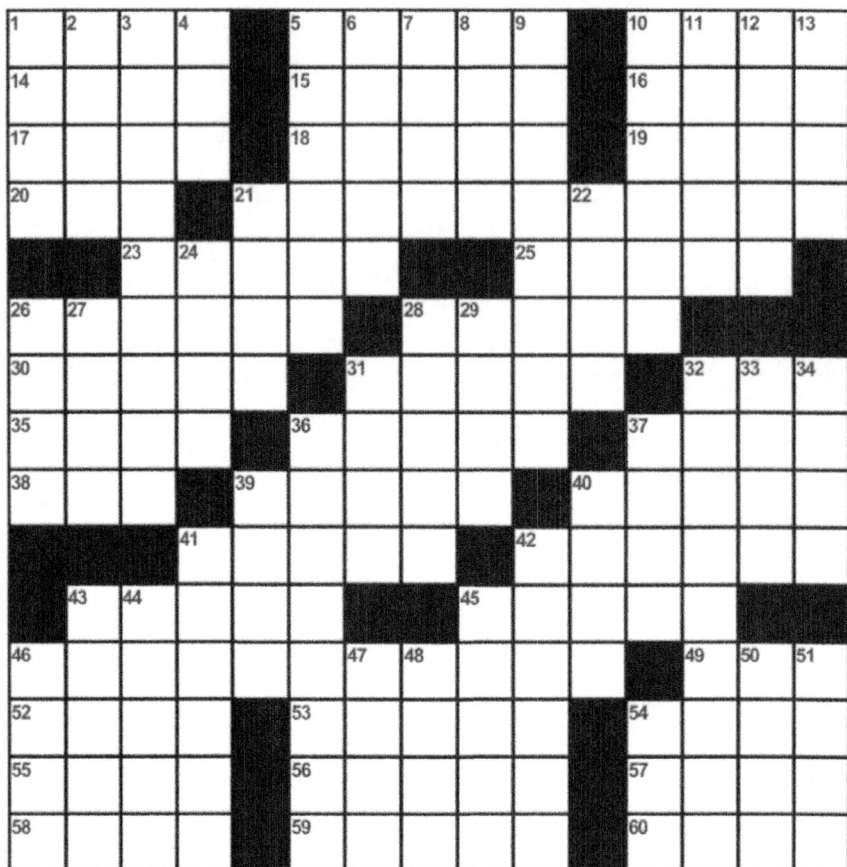

ACROSS

1) Composer Alban
5) ___ Cove ("Murder, She Wrote" setting)
10) Put in a snit
14) Shampoo additive
15) Immature egg, to a zoologist
16) Hosiery shade
17) Turn on the waterworks
18) White oak of California
19) Hammer-wielding god
20) "The ___ is in sight"
21) Tries mightily to get ashore?
23) Wrinkle removers
25) Deck out
26) Canal country
28) Agra airs
30) Monarch's loyal subject
31) It talks, it's said
32) You can take it or beat it
35) "So what ___ is new?"
36) Consumer

DOWN

1) George Herman Ruth, familiarly
2) Distinctive and stylish elegance
3) Disorderliness
4) Foam alternative for shavers
5) Sun's circle of light
6) Swears
7) Macs
8) Southwest crock pot
9) Many a new driver
10) Some public-transit systems, briefly
11) Mythological blood
12) Displeased look
13) Minks and sables
21) It wasn't built in a day
22) June 6, 1944
24) Be furious
26) Urgent request
27) Feels achy
28) Helicopter blade
29) From square one
31) Untouchable, in mafia lingo
32) Some urban dwellings

33) Downwind, for a ship
34) Lemon skin
36) Gives over for safekeeping
37) No longer working (abbr.)
39) Capital of Italy
40) ___-up (confined)
41) Plea at sea
42) Lacks humility
43) Bat's detection tool
44) Light rope
45) Hollowed, as an apple
46) Tenant's payment
47) It might wind up on shore
48) Cause of harm
50) Lumber cutters
51) Bertie Wooster's Agatha, for one
54) Sixth sense

ACROSS

37) Part in a movie
38) Horse's cousin
39) Furnish, as with talent
40) Small flycatcher
41) Remote control, at times
42) House of worship
43) One of the Beatles
45) High-rise unit
46) Command to Michael
49) OPEC's largest customer
52) "National Velvet" author Bagnold
53) Big-time retailer

54) Grandson of Abraham
55) Sha ___ (doo-wop group)
56) Guiding doctrine
57) In stitches
58) Three-pip card
59) Goes tirelessly?
60) "I've got a secret to tell you"

17 STICKS ARE ARRANGED AS IN THE ATTACHED IMAGE TO FORM 6 SQUARES. IF I TAKE 5 STICKS, WE WILL BE LEFT WITH ONLY 3 SQUARES.

CAN YOU FIND THE ANSWER IN 30 SECONDS?

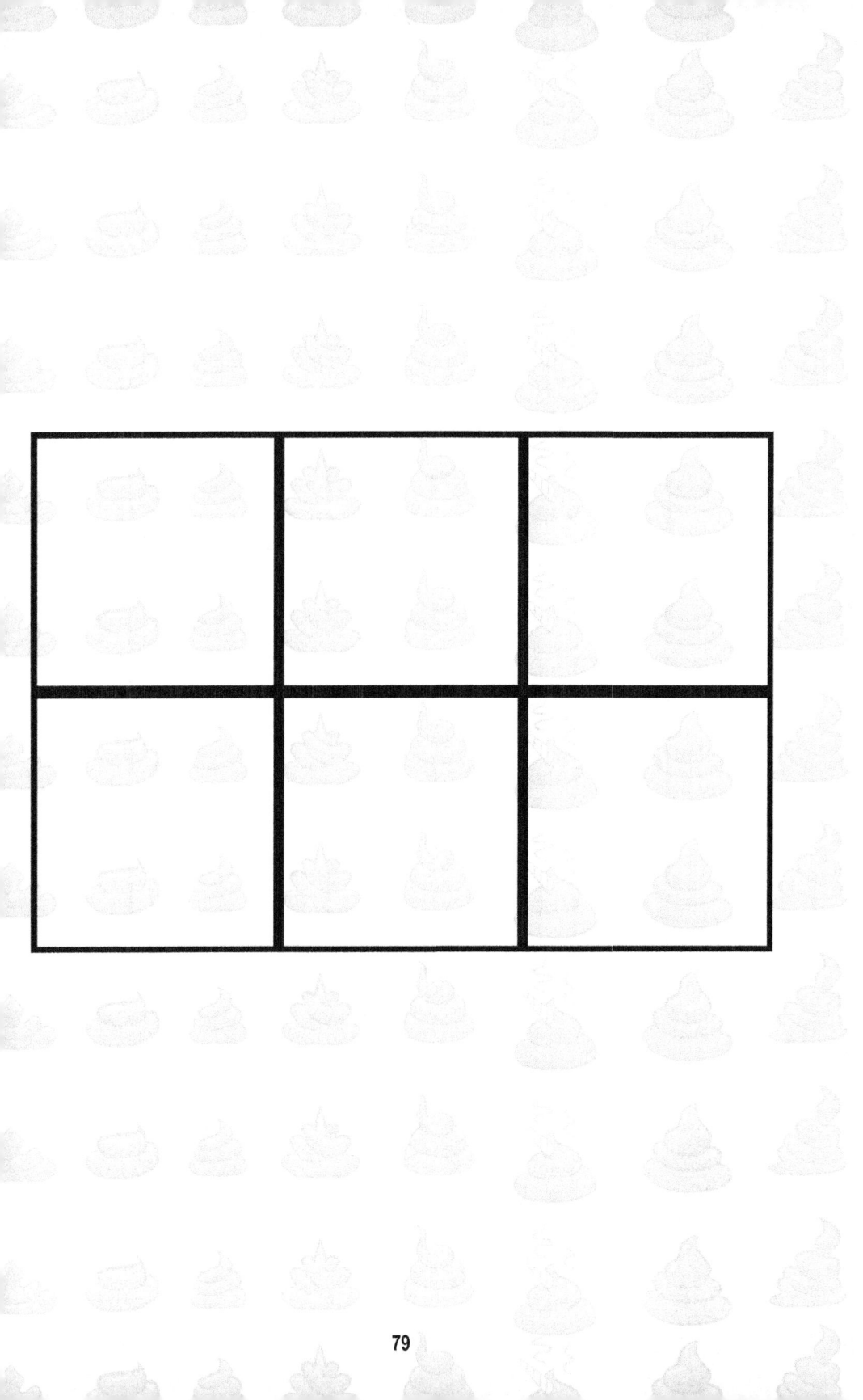

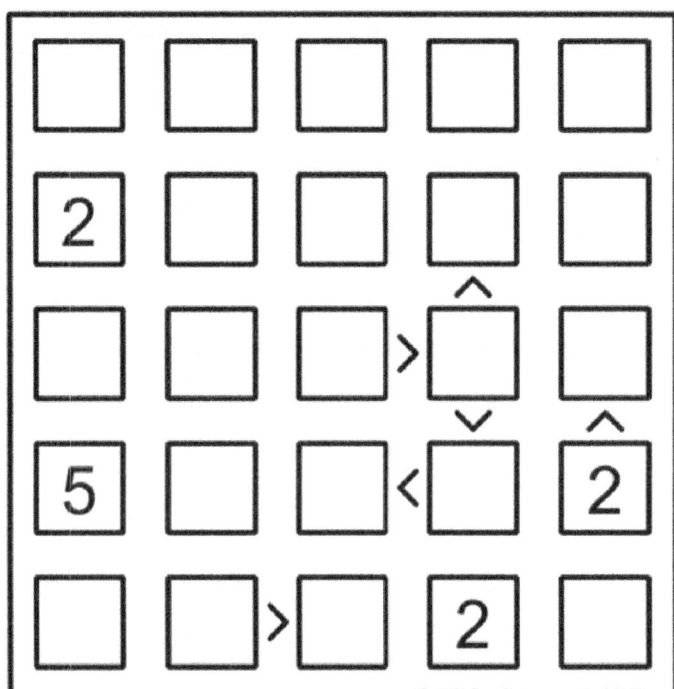

USE SIX NINES TO GIVE YOU 100.

LET'S SEE IF YOU SUCCEED IN 60 SECONDS. START NOW!

YOU HAVE ELEVEN MATCHES.
PLACE THEM IN SUCH A WAY THAT
THERE ARE NINE OF THEM.

NOW YOU HAVE THREE MATCHES.
PLACE THEM ON THE TABLE SO
THAT THERE ARE FOUR OF THEM.

WHY DID THE TOILET BREAK UP WITH THE BATHTUB?

IT COULDN'T DEAL WITH ALL THE DRAINING ISSUES.

WHAT'S A SKELETON'S LEAST FAVORITE ROOM IN THE HOUSE?

THE BATHROOM – THERE ARE TOO MANY "CRACKS" IN THE WALL!

WHY DID THE SHOWER GO TO THERAPY?

IT HAD TOO MANY ISSUES WITH ITS DRAIN.

BATHROOM

bath-rüm [NOUN]

A temporary sanctuary for overwhelmed parents seeking refuge from their offspring.

p2

p3

$$9 \times 8 + 7 + 6 + 5 + 4 + 3 + 2 + 1 = 100$$

p6

1. A STITCH IN TIME SAVES NINE.
2. FAINT HEART NEVER WON FAIR LADY.
3. STRIKE WHILE THE IRON'S HOT.
4. HE LAUGHS BEST WHO LAUGHS LAST.
5. BIRDS OF A FEATHER FLOCK TOGETHER.
6. HE WHO GOES A BORROWING GOES A SORROWING.

p8

p10

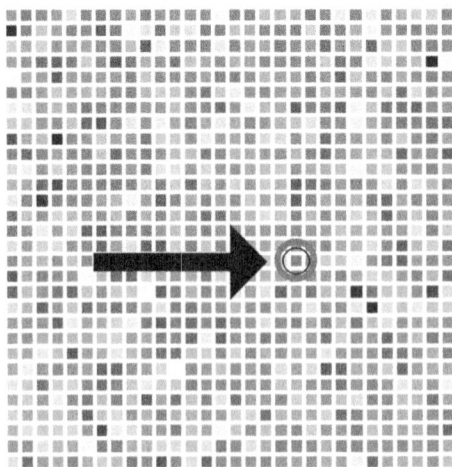

p12

egiDlht	DELIGHT	rCimhasa	CHARISMA
amnulelitl	ILLUMINATE	lieGagrnn	GLEAMING
anromouisH	HARMONIOUS	tnejvaReue	REJUVENATE
ebiuleJ	JUBILEE	elyvLi	LIVELY
upraeEnrt	ENRAPTURE	tqeixsuIE	EXQUISITE
anRdciae	RADIANCE	yRasdohp	RHAPSODY
wdWilnhir	WHIRLWIND	eihvrT	THRIVE
stZe	ZEST	soicuVvia	VIVACIOUS
ubnicaeJl	JUBILANCE	cEtssay	ECSTASY
mSeiblu	SUBLIME	ciproEuh	EUPHORIC
rhpycZ	ZEPHYR	sinEovin	ENVISION
rtinglGeti	GLITTERING	giraMe	MIRAGE
eNcart	NECTAR	Ossai	OASIS
nltfneii	INFINITE	otUpai	UTOPIA
tacliDee	DELICATE	Gmela	GLEAM
vigenraolt	INVIGORATE	zQlziauci	QUIZZICAL
goytrraCpm	CRYPTOGRAM	loWirstd	WORDLIST
Mysytre	MYSTERY	epPreix	PERPLEX
onpyrEt	ENTROPY	Srtam	SMART
Cervle	CLEVER	ealnMt	MENTAL

p16

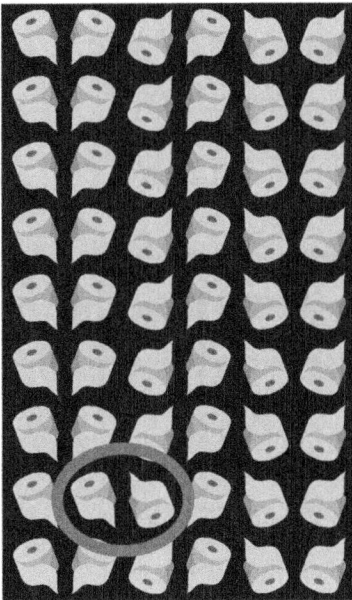

p18

p14

p20

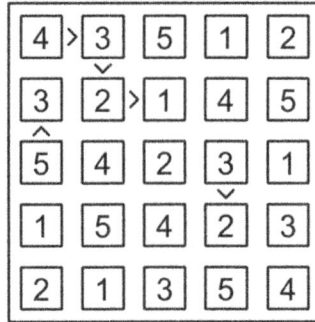

p22

P26

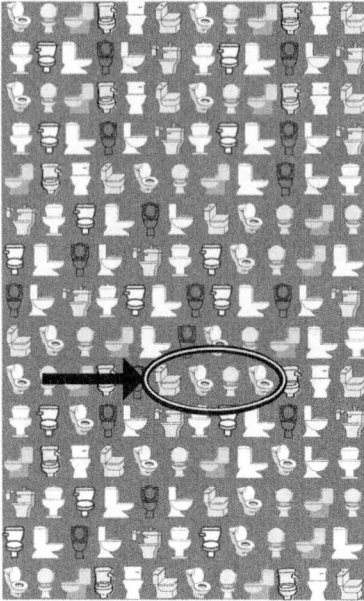

P30

dAreutvne	ADVENTURE	hSnseiun	SUNSHINE
arerancgF	FRAGRANCE	nEpletah	ELEPHANT
nhSpoymy	SYMPHONY	uftIreytB	BUTTERFLY
caetoohCl	CHOCOLATE	itoeatnMdi	MEDITATION
aHenspisp	HAPPINESS	srUvniee	UNIVERSE
tnliuTyriaq	TRANQUILITY	npedytrieSi	SERENDIPITY
hmtEnssaui	ENTHUSIASM	Piobtiyssil	POSSIBILITY
Crtuiiyso	CURIOSITY	cfetnioe!R	REFLECTION
nVratib	VIBRANT	uaionibljt	JUBILATION
yaHonmr	HARMONY	edorWn	WONDER
gtLeruha	LAUGHTER	rpihFisden	FRIENDSHIP
mssoBlo	BLOSSOM	uhiEoarp	EUPHORIA
ovalerMsu	MARVELOUS	tintgCipaav	CAPTIVATING
klraeSp	SPARKLE	iadtRan	RADIANT
yodMle	MELODY	eCscaad	CASCADE
closuaiMru	MIRACULOUS	Dtguefhlii	DELIGHTFUL
dmorFee	FREEDOM	ieyeSrnt	SERENITY
mosiunLu	LUMINOUS	ieeenslRic	RESILIENCE
Tiaqlnur	TRANQUIL	danlndoWre	WONDERLAND
Bintilrla	BRILLIANT	anrispniolt	INSPIRATION

P28

P32

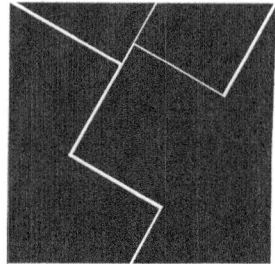

P34

2	9	4
7	5	3
6	1	8

P35

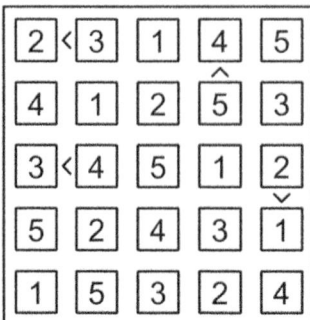

88

C	A	S	A	S		M	U	T	T		O	R	B	S
O	S	H	E	A		A	C	R	E		C	U	R	E
R	E	I	G	N		U	L	A	N		T	B	A	R
D	A	V	I	D	B	L	A	I	N	E		B	E	E
			S	A	L			L	I	T	H	E		
L	A	O		L	E	S	S		S	H	O	R	T	S
A	L	V	A		A	N	T	I		A	L	T	H	O
S	I	E	G	F	R	I	E	D	A	N	D	R	O	Y
S	E	R	R	A		T	A	L	L		S	E	R	A
O	N	S	E	T	S		D	E	A	F		E	N	S
		H	E	A	L	S			M	E	T			
P	S	A		L	A	N	C	E	B	U	R	T	O	N
R	O	D	S		L	A	B	S		D	I	A	N	A
I	D	O	L		O	R	E	S		A	P	R	E	S
M	A	W	R		M	E	R	E		L	E	A	S	H

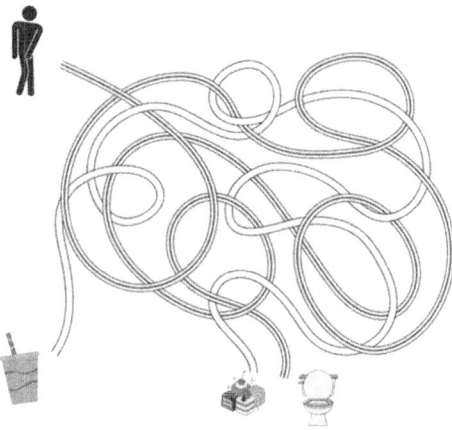

P	Q	P	G	U	E	R	J	A	Y	B
A	J	D	D	C	L	I	E	J	E	D
M	M	S	M	K	F	R	O	A	S	Q
P	R	S	S	O	L	F	Q	P	D	X
E	J	A	M	A	U	H	L	M	P	A
R	E	W	O	H	S	V	O	M	T	L
F	V	A	E	U	H	C	N	D	R	E
U	A	T	R	B	A	G	R	C	E	R
Q	H	B	F	C	H	D	C	U	M	P
D	S	I	N	G	B	J	T	M	B	I
P	S	Y	Y	E	L	D	U	Q	Y	Y

Wchislmai	WHIMSICAL	Buslsilf	BLISSFUL
eeEetncvsffr	EFFERVESCENT	gnMcteiinfa	MAGNIFICENT
bnoRwia	RAINBOW	meScarlb	SCRAMBLE
zzuelP	PUZZLE	bmelJu	JUMBLE
Aarmgna	ANAGRAM	eesrtLt	LETTERS
snleabrUcm	UNSCRAMBLE	rBian	BRAIN
olWpyrad	WORDPLAY	aegaLnug	LANGUAGE
eClu	CLUE	eagCllehn	CHALLENGE
Regeaanrr	REARRANGE	lroaayucbV	VOCABULARY
Wrmtodsih	WORDSMITH	uonsfeC	CONFUSE
fSuhfle	SHUFFLE	uesGs	GUESS
iMpxu	MIXUP	gviSoln	SOLVING
Txet	TEXT	tBnomarsri	BRAINSTORM
esaeT	TEASE	utiLsgsiinc	LINGUISTICS
idedRl	RIDDLE	oraedWgm	WORDGAME
gEmina	ENIGMA	pcrheeDi	DECIPHER
twsTi	TWIST	iptxteerCh	CIPHERTEXT
rteSce	SECRET	nidHde	HIDDEN
eCdo	CODE	odmaRn	RANDOM
iLecnox	LEXICON	tiycioDnra	DICTIONARY

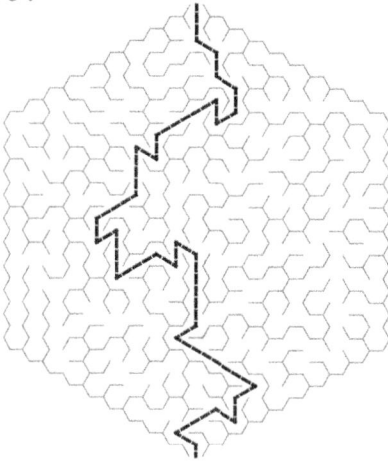

THE FIRST NUMBER IS 8.
$$8+2=10$$

THE SECOND IS 12.
$$12-2=10$$

THE THIRD IS 5.
$$5 \times 2=10$$

THE FOURTH IS 20.
$$20 \div 2=10$$

$$8+12+5+20=45$$

1 A	2 S	3 T	4 I	R	5 M	6 A	7 C	8 A	W	9 R	10 A	11 T
12 L	L	A	N	O	13 U	V	U	L	A	14 A	P	E
15 B	A	C	O	16 N	S	R	E	B	E	17 L	L	I	O	N
18 U	P	O	N		19 R	A	R	E		20 L	I	N	G	O
21 M	O	M		22 S	I	L	T		23 F	E	E	D	E	R
24 S	N	A	F	U			25 O	A	T		26 R	E	S
		27 R	E	A	28 D	A	P	T		29 S	O	S
	30 L	E	T	T	U	C	E	W	31 R	A	P
32 P	I	E		33 T	O	E	N	A	I	L
34 V	A	N		35 C	I	S			36 F	E	T	C	H
37 I	P	E	C	A	C		38 T	H	A	T		39 A	H	A
40 R	O	S	I	N		41 E	R	I	N		42 S	K	E	W
43 T	O	M	A	T	O	V	A	R	I	E	T	I	E	S
44 U	S	A		45 O	N	I	C	E		46 M	A	N	S	E
47 E	E	N		48 R	O	L	E	S		49 U	R	G	E	S

4	2	1 < 3	5
1	3	2	5	4
3	4 < 5	2	1
2	5	4	1 < 3
5	1	3	4	2

A. ROLLING STONES GATHER NO MOSS.
B. PROCRASTINATION IS THE THIEF OF TIME.
C. TIME AND TIDE WAIT FOR NO MAN.
D. A BIRD IN THE HAND IS WORTH TWO IN THE BUSH.

THE NUMBER IS 37:

37x3=111
37x6=222
37x9=333
37x12=444
37x15=555
37x18=666
37x21=777
37x24=888
37x27=999

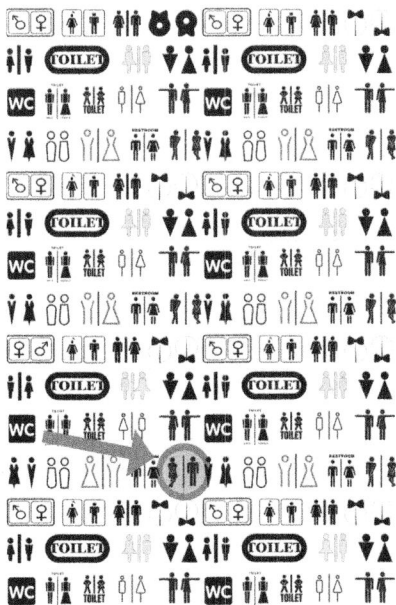

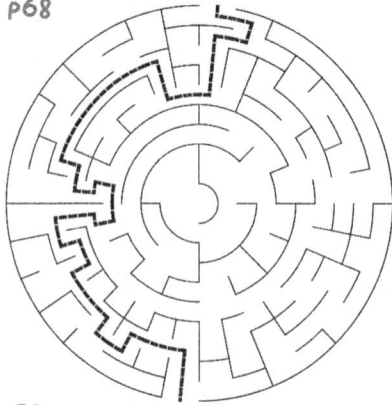

PERSEVERE YE PERFECT MEN,
EVER KEEP THESE PRECEPTS TEN.

nleipgSl	SPELLING	kciTry	TRICKY
laPfluy	PLAYFUL	lteecnIgnlie	INTELLIGENCE
iulntpMaea	MANIPULATE	Cyxtliepom	COMPLEXITY
Docsevyir	DISCOVERY	idbrndeenM	MINDBENDER
veriCeta	CREATIVE	llCinheggan	CHALLENGING
uFn	FUN	nilgture	INTRIGUE
eMtisrsouy	MYSTERIOUS	binaelerotC	CELEBRATION
mgcatiEni	ENIGMATIC	iCtrvaitye	CREATIVITY
ieSpnddl	SPLENDID	oAinbmti	AMBITION
Dmcaiyn	DYNAMIC	olesignun	INGENIOUS
Groeusog	GORGEOUS	utZslfe	ZESTFUL
inolnonvta	INNOVATION	Gsloouir	GLORIOUS
arouCogsue	COURAGEOUS	cinnEnthga	ENCHANTING
aulntjib	JUBILANT	nenahePlmo	PHENOMENAL
nxuEbaetr	EXUBERANT	vaerlM	MARVEL
ntligrugni	INTRIGUING	ovaSr	SAVOR
feGacrul	GRACEFUL	ertlheEa	ETHEREAL
yrroPtpies	PROSPERITY	eArull	ALLURE
veeReir	REVERIE	rldeonpS	SPLENDOR
nPinaelc	PINNACLE	Firolhsu	FLOURISH

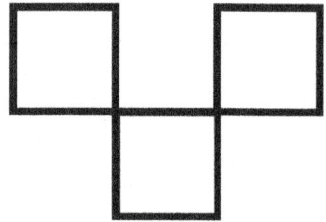

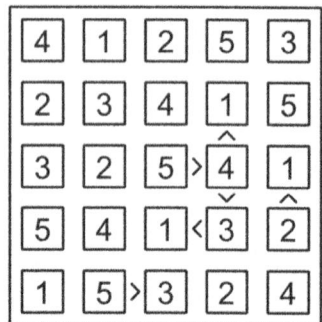

$$99 + \frac{99}{99} = 100$$

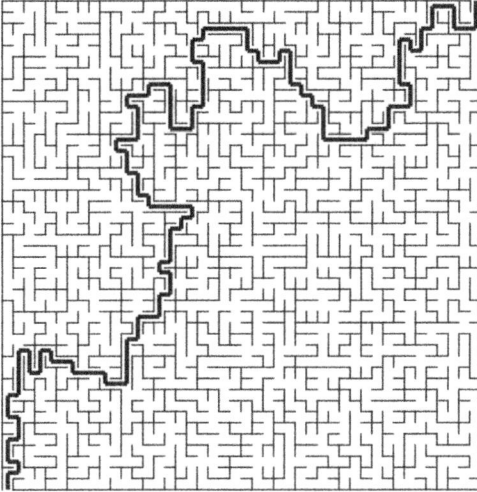

PLACE THEM SO AS TO FORM THE WORD <u>NINE</u>.

PLACE THEM SO AS TO FORM THE ROMAN NUMBER <u>IV</u>.

WHAT HAPPENS in the bathroom STAYS IN THE BATHROOM

PLEASE DON'T FORGET TO REVIEW MY BOOK AND SUGGEST WHAT WE CAN CREATE FOR YOU NEXT.

YES, I DID READ ALL MY COMMENTS!

SCAN THIS QR TO REVIEW

THANKS FOR YOUR HONEST INPUT, WHICH HELPS US IMPROVE FUTURE PUBLICATIONS.

FROM THE SAME SERIES:

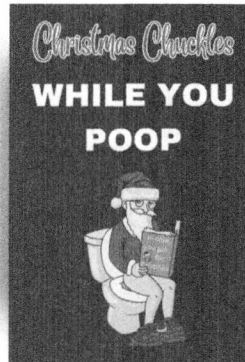

WHILE YOU POOP

WHILE YOU POOP FISHING EDITION

Christmas Chuckles WHILE YOU POOP

WHILE YOU POOP CRYPTOGRAMS

Printed in Great Britain
by Amazon